Human Origins

RICHARD L...

A Phoenix Paperback
First published in Great Britain by Weidenfeld & Nicolson in 1994
as *The Origin of Humankind* (Science Masters series)
Paperback edition published in 1995

This abridged edition published in 1996 by Phoenix
A division of Orion Books Ltd
Orion House, 5 Upper St Martin's Lane, London WC2H 9EA

This abridged edition contains the Preface and Chapters 5 and 6
(without line drawings or maps).

Cover illustration: Photograph of a human skull with sections of bone
removed from the skull and jawbone to reveal the roots of the upper and
lower teeth © John Watney/Science Photo Library

ISBN 1 85799 617 8

Typeset by Deltatype Ltd, Ellesmere Port, Cheshire
Printed in Great Britain by Clays Ltd, St Ives plc

CONTENTS

Preface

It is every anthropologist's dream to unearth a complete skeleton of an ancient human ancestor. For most of us, however, that dream remains unfulfilled: the vagaries of death, burial, and fossilization conspire to leave a meager, fragmented record of human prehistory. Isolated teeth, single bones, fragments of skulls: for the most part, these are the clues from which the story of human prehistory must be reconstructed. I don't deny the importance of such clues, frustratingly incomplete though they are; without them, there would be little to tell of the story of human prehistory. Nor do I discount the raw excitement of experiencing the physical presence of these modest relics; they are part of our ancestry, linked to us by countless generations of flesh and blood. But the discovery of a complete skeleton remains the ultimate prize.

In 1969, I was blessed with extraordinary good fortune. I had determined to explore the ancient sandstone deposits that make up the vast eastern shore of Lake Turkana, in northern Kenya – my first independent foray into fossil country. I was driven by a strong conviction that major fossil discoveries would be made there, because I had flown over the region in a small plane a year earlier: I recognized that the layered deposits were potential repositories of ancient life – though many doubted my judgment. The terrain is rugged and the climate unrelentingly hot and dry; moreover, the landscape has the kind of fierce beauty that appeals to me.

With the support of the National Geographic Society, I assembled a small team – including Meave Epps, who later became my wife – to explore the region. One morning several days after we had arrived, Meave and I were returning to our camp from a short prospecting excursion, by way of a shortcut along a dry riverbed, both of us thirsty and anxious to avoid the searing heat of midday. Suddenly, I saw directly ahead of us an intact, fossilized skull resting on the orange sand, its eye sockets staring at us blankly. It was unmistakably human in shape. Although the passing years have robbed my memory of exactly what I said to Meave at that instant, I know I expressed a mixture of joy and disbelief at what we had stumbled upon.

The cranium, which I immediately recognized as that of *Australopithecus boisei*, a long-extinct human species, had only recently emerged from the sediments through which the seasonal river coursed. Exposed to the sunlight for the first time since the elements buried it almost 1.75 million years ago, the specimen was one of the few intact ancient human skulls that had yet been found. Within weeks of its exposure, heavy rains would fill the dry bed with a raging torrent; if Meave and I had not come upon it, the fragile relic would certainly have been destroyed by the flood. The chances of our being there at the right time to recover the long-buried fossil for science were minuscule.

By a curious coincidence, my discovery occurred a decade, almost to the day, after my mother, Mary Leakey, had found a similar cranium at Olduvai Gorge, in Tanzania. (That cranium, however, was a daunting Paleolithic jigsaw puzzle; it had to be reconstructed from hundreds of fragments.) Apparently I had inherited the legendary 'Leakey luck,' enjoyed so notably by Mary and my father, Louis. And indeed my good fortune held, as subsequent expeditions I led to Lake Turkana turned up many more human fossils, including the oldest-known intact cranium of the genus *Homo*, the branch of the human family that eventually gave rise to modern humans, *Homo sapiens*.

Although as a youth I had vowed not to become involved in fossil hunting – wishing to avoid being in the considerable shadow of my world-famous parents – the sheer magic of the enterprise drew me into it. The ancient, arid deposits of East Africa that entomb the remains of our ancestors have an undeniable, special beauty, yet they are unforgiving and dangerous, too. The search for fossils and ancient stone tools is often presented as a romantic experience, and it certainly possesses its romantic aspects, but it is a science where the fundamental data have to be recovered hundreds or thousands of miles distant from the comfort of the laboratory. It is a physically challenging and demanding enterprise – a logistical operation upon which the safety of people's lives sometimes depends. I found that I had a talent for organization, for getting things done in the face of difficult personal and physical circumstances. The many important discoveries from the eastern shore of Lake Turkana not only seduced me into a profession I had once vehemently eschewed but also established my reputation in it. Nevertheless, the ultimate dream – a complete skeleton – continued to elude me.

In the late summer of 1984, with our collective breaths held and our steadily building hope tempered by the hard reality of experience, my colleagues and I saw that dream begin to take shape. That year we had decided to explore for the first time the western shore of the lake. On August 23rd, Kamoya Kimeu, my oldest friend and colleague, spotted a small fragment of an ancient cranium lying among pebbles on a slope near a narrow gully that had been sculpted by a seasonal stream. Carefully we began a search for further fragments of the skull and soon found more than we dared hope for. During the five seasons of excavation that followed this find, amounting to more than seven months in the field, our team moved fifteen hundred tons of sediment in the massive search. We uncovered what eventually turned out to be virtually the entire skeleton of an individual who had died at the edge of the ancient lake, more than 1.5 million years ago. Dubbed by us the Turkana boy, he was barely nine years old when he died; the cause of his death remains a mystery.

It was a truly extraordinary experience to unearth fossil

bone after fossil bone: arms, legs, vertebrae, ribs, pelvis, jaw, teeth, and more cranium. The boy's skeleton began to take shape, reconstructed as an individual once again after lying in fragments for sixteen hundred millennia. Nothing as complete as this skeleton is found in the human fossil record until Neanderthal times, a mere 100,000 years ago. Quite apart from the emotional thrill of such a find, we were aware that the discovery promised great insight into a critical phase of human prehistory.

A word, before I go on with the story, about jargon in anthropology. Sometimes the blizzard of arcane terms can be so fierce as to defy comprehension by all but the most dedicated professionals. I will avoid such jargon, as far as is possible. Each of the various species of the prehistoric human family has a scientific label – that is, its species name – and we can't avoid using these. The human family of species has a label of its own, too: hominid. Some of my colleagues prefer to use the term 'hominid' for all ancestral human species. The word 'human,' they argue, should be used to refer only to people like us. In other words, the only hominids to be designated 'human' are those that display our own level of intelligence, moral sense, and depth of introspective consciousness.

I take a different view. It seems to me that the evolution of upright locomotion, which distinguished ancient hominids from other apes of the time, was fundamental to subsequent human history. Once our distant ancestor became a bipedal ape, many other evolutionary innovations became possible, with the eventual appearance of *Homo*. For this reason, I believe that we are justified in calling all hominid species 'human.' By this I do not mean to suggest that all ancient human species experienced the mental worlds we know today. At its most basic, the designation 'human' simply refers to apes that walked upright – bipedal apes. I will adopt this usage in the following pages, and will indicate when I am using it to describe features that characterize only modern man.

The Turkana boy was a member of the species *Homo erectus* – a species pivotal in the history of human evolution. From different lines of evidence – some genetic, some fossil – we know that the first human species evolved about 7 million years ago. By the time *Homo erectus* arrived on the scene, almost 2 million years ago, human prehistory was already well along. We don't yet know how many human species lived and died before the appearance of *Homo erectus*: there were at least six, and perhaps twice that number. We do know, however, that all human species living prior to *Homo erectus* were, although bipedal, distinctly apelike in many respects. They had relatively small brains, their faces were prognathous (that is, they jutted forward), and the shape of their bodies was more apelike than human in particular features, such as a funnel-shaped chest, little neck, and no waist. In *Homo erectus*, brain size increased, the face was flatter, and the body was more athletically built. The evolution of *Homo erectus* brought with it many of the physical characteristics we recognize in ourselves: human prehistory evidently took a major turn 2 million years ago.

Homo erectus was the first human species to use fire; the first to include hunting as a significant part of its subsistence; the first to be able to run as modern humans do; the first to make stone tools according to some definite mental template; and the first to extend its range beyond Africa. We don't know definitively whether *Homo erectus* possessed a degree of spoken language, but several lines of evidence suggest this. And we don't know, and probably never will know, whether this species experienced a degree of self-awareness, a humanlike consciousness, but my guess is that it did. Needless to say, language and consciousness, which are among the most prized features of *Homo sapiens*, leave no trace in the prehistoric record.

The anthropologist's goal is to understand the evolutionary events that transformed an apelike creature into people like us. These events have been described, romantically, as a great drama, with emerging humanity as the hero of the tale. The truth is probably more prosaic, with climatic and ecological modification rather than epic adventure driving the change. The transformation arrests our attention no less for all that. As a species, we are blessed with a curiosity about the world of nature and our place in it. We want to know – *need* to know – how we came to be as we are, and what our future is. The fossils we find connect us physically to our past and challenge us to interpret the clues they embody as a way of understanding the nature and course of our evolutionary history.

Until many more relics of human prehistory have been unearthed and analyzed, no anthropologist can stand up and declare, This is how it was in every detail. There is, however, a great deal of agreement among researchers about the overall shape of human prehistory. In it, four key stages can be confidently identified.

The first was the origin of the human family itself, some 7 million years ago, when an apelike species with a bipedal, or upright, mode of locomotion evolved. The second stage was the proliferation of bipedal species, a process that biologists call adaptive radiation. Between 7 million and 2 million years ago, many different species of bipedal ape evolved, each adapted to slightly different ecological circumstances. Among this proliferation of human species was one that, between 3 million and 2 million years ago, developed a significantly larger brain. The expansion in brain size marks the third stage, and signals the origin of the genus *Homo*, the branch of the human bush that led through *Homo erectus* and ultimately to *Homo sapiens*. The fourth stage was the origin of modern humans – the evolution of people like ourselves, fully equipped with language, consciousness, artistic imagination, and technological innovation unseen elsewhere in nature.

These four key events provide the structure for the scientific narrative in the book that follows. As will become evident, in our study of human prehistory we are beginning to ask not only *what* happened, and *when*, but also *why* things happened. We and our ancestors are being studied in the context of an unfolding evolutionary scenario, just as we would study the evolution of elephants or horses. This is not to deny that *Homo sapiens* is special in many ways: much separates us from even our closest evolutionary relative, the chimpanzee, but we have begun to understand our connection with nature in a biological sense.

The past three decades have witnessed tremendous advances in our science, the result of unprecedented fossil discoveries and innovative ways of interpreting and integrating the clues we see in them. Like all sciences, anthropology is subject to honest, and sometimes vigorous, differences of opinion among its practitioners. These stem sometimes from insufficient data, in the form of fossils and stone tools, and sometimes from inadequacies of methods of interpretation. There are therefore many important questions about human history for which there are no definitive answers, such as: What is the precise shape of the human family tree? When did sophisticated spoken language first evolve? What caused the dramatic increase in brain size in human prehistory? In the following chapters, I will indicate where, and why, differences of opinion exist, and sometimes I will offer my own preference. . . .

The Origin of Modern Humans

Of the four major events in the course of human evolution which I outlined in the preface – the origin of the human family itself, some 7 million years ago; the subsequent 'adaptive radiation' of species of bipedal apes; the origin of the enlarged brain (effectively, the beginning of the genus *Homo*), perhaps 2.5 million years ago; and the origin of modern humans – it is the fourth, the origin of people like us, that is currently the hottest issue in anthropology. Very different hypotheses are vigorously debated, and hardly a month passes without a conference being held or a shower of books and scientific papers being published, each of these putting forward views that are often diametrically opposed. By 'people like us' I mean modern *Homo sapiens* – that is, humans with a flair for technology and innovation, a capacity for artistic expression, an introspective consciousness, and a sense of morality.

As we look back into history just a few thousand years, we see the initial emergence of civilization: in social organization of greater and greater complexity, villages give way to chiefdoms, chiefdoms give way to city-states, city-states give way to nation-states. This seemingly inexorable rise in the level of complexity is driven by cultural evolution, not by biological change. Just as people a century ago were like us biologically but occupied a world without electronic technology, so the villagers of 7000 years ago were just like us but lacking in the infrastructure of civilization.

If we look back into history beyond the origin of writing, some 6000 years ago, we can still see evidence of the modern human mind at work. Beginning about 10,000 years ago, nomadic bands of hunter-gatherers throughout the world independently invented various agricultural techniques. This, too, was the consequence of cultural or technological, not biological, evolution. Go back beyond that time of social and economic transformation and you find the paintings, engravings, and carvings of Ice Age Europe and of Africa, which evoke the mental worlds of people like us. Go back beyond this, however – beyond about 35,000 years ago – and these beacons of the modern human mind gutter out. No longer can we see in the archeological record cogent evidence of the work of people with mental capacities like our own.

For a long time, anthropologists believed that the sudden appearance of artistic expression and finely crafted technology in the archeological record some 35,000 years ago was a clear signal of the evolution of modern humans. The British anthropologist Kenneth Oakley was among the first to suggest, in 1951, that this efflorescence of modern human behavior was associated with the first appearance of fully modern language. Indeed, it seems inconceivable that a species of human could possess fully modern language and not be fully modern in all other ways, too. For this reason, the evolution of language is widely judged to be the culminating event in the emergence of humanity as we know it to be today.

When did the origin of modern humans occur? And in what manner did it happen: gradually and beginning a long time ago, or rapidly and recently? These questions are at the core of the current debate.

Ironically, of all the periods of human evolution, that of the past several hundred thousand years is by far the most richly endowed with fossil evidence. In addition to an extensive collection of intact crania and postcranial bones, some twenty relatively complete skeletons have been recovered. To someone like me, whose preoccupation is with an earlier period in human prehistory, in which fossil evidence is sparse, these are paleontological riches in the extreme. And yet a consensus on the sequence of evolutionary events still eludes my anthropological colleagues.

Moreover, the very first early human fossils ever discovered were of Neanderthals (everyone's favorite caricature of cavemen), who play an important role in the debate. Since 1856, when the first Neanderthal bones were uncovered, the fate of these people has been endlessly discussed: Were they our immediate ancestors or an evolutionary dead end that slipped into extinction some thirty millennia before the present? This question was posed almost a century ago, and is still unanswered, at least to everyone's satisfaction.

Before we delve into some of the finer points of the argument over the origin of modern humans, we should outline the larger issues. The story begins with the evolution of the genus *Homo*, prior to 2 million years ago, and ends with the ultimate appearance of *Homo sapiens*. Two lines of evidence have long existed: one concerning anatomical changes and the other concerning changes in technology and other manifestations of the human brain and hand. Rendered correctly, these two lines of evidence should illustrate the same story of human evolutionary history. They should indicate the same pattern of change through time. These traditional lines of evidence, the stuff of anthropological scholarship for decades, have recently been joined by a third, that of molecular genetics. In principle, genetic evidence has encrypted within it an account of our evolutionary history. Again, the story it tells should accord with what we learn from anatomy and stone tools.

Unfortunately, there is no state of harmony among these three lines of evidence. There are points of connection but no consensus. The difficulty anthropologists face even with such an abundance of evidence is a salutary reminder of how very difficult it often is to reconstruct evolutionary history.

The discovery of the Turkana boy's skeleton gives us an

excellent idea of the anatomy of early man some 1.6 million years ago. We can see that early *Homo erectus* individuals were tall (the Turkana boy stood at close to 6 feet), athletic, and powerfully muscled. Even the strongest modern professional wrestler would have been a poor match for the average *Homo erectus*. Although the brain of early *Homo erectus* was larger than that of its australopithecine forebears, it was still smaller than that of modern humans – some 900 cubic centimeters compared with the average 1350 cubic centimeters of *Homo* today. The cranium of *Homo erectus* is long and low, with little forehead and a thick skull; the jaws protrude somewhat, and above the eyes are prominent ridges. This basic anatomical pattern persisted until about half a million years ago, although there was an expansion of the brain during this time to more than 1100 cubic centimeters. By this time, *Homo erectus* populations had spread out from Africa and were occupying large regions of Asia and Europe. (While no unequivocally identified *Homo erectus* fossils have been found in Europe, evidence of technology associated with the species betrays its presence there.)

More recently than about 34,000 years ago, the fossil human remains we find are all those of fully modern *Homo sapiens*. The body is less rugged and muscular, the face flatter, the cranium higher, and the skull wall thinner. The brow ridges are not prominent, and the brain (for the most part) is larger. We can see, therefore, that the evolutionary activity giving rise to modern humans took place in the interval between half a million years ago and 34,000 years ago. From what we find in Africa and Eurasia in the fossil and archeological record of that interval, we can conclude that evolution was indeed active but in confusing ways.

The Neanderthals lived from about 135,000 to 34,000 years ago, and occupied a region stretching from Western Europe through the Near East and into Asia. They constitute by far the most abundant component of the fossil record for the period we are interested in here. There is no question that ripples of evolution were going on in many different populations throughout the Old World during this period of half a million to 34,000 years ago. Aside from the Neanderthals, there are individual fossils – usually crania or parts of crania, but sometimes other parts of the skeleton – with romantic-sounding names: Petralona Man, from Greece; Arago Man, from southwestern France; Steinheim Man, from Germany; Broken Hill Man, from Zambia; and so on. Despite many differences among these individual specimens, they all have two things in common: they are more advanced than *Homo erectus* – having larger brains, for instance – and more primitive than *Homo sapiens*, being thick-skulled and robustly built. Because of the varying anatomy of the specimens from this period, anthropologists have taken to labeling these fossils collectively as 'archaic *sapiens*.'

The challenge we face, given this potpourri of anatomical form, is to construct an evolutionary pattern that describes the emergence of modern human anatomy and behavior. In recent years, two very different models have been proposed.

The first of them, known as the multiregional-evolution hypothesis, sees the origin of modern humans as a phenomenon encompassing the entire Old World, with *Homo sapiens* emerging wherever populations of *Homo erectus* had become established. In this view, the Neanderthals are part of that three-continent-wide trend, intermediate in anatomy between *Homo erectus* and modern *Homo sapiens* in Europe, the Middle East, and western Asia, and today's populations in those parts of the Old World had Neanderthals as direct ancestors. Milford Wolpoff, an anthropologist at the University of Michigan, argues that the ubiquitous evolutionary trend toward the biological status of *Homo sapiens* was driven by the new cultural milieu of our ancestors.

Culture represents a novelty in the world of nature, and it could have added an effective, unifying edge to the forces of natural selection. Moreover, Christopher Wills, a biologist at the University of California, Santa Cruz, identifies the possibility here of an accelerating pace of evolution. In his 1993 book *The Runaway Brain*, he notes: 'The force that seems to have accelerated our brain's growth is a new kind of stimulant: language, signs, collective memories – all elements of culture. As our cultures evolved in complexities, so did our brains, which then drove our cultures to still greater complexity. Big and clever brains led to more complex cultures, which in turn led to yet bigger and cleverer brains.' If such an autocatalytic, or positive feedback, process did occur, it could help promulgate genetic change through large populations more rapidly.

I have some sympathy with the multiregional evolution view, and once offered the following analogy: If you take a handful of pebbles and fling them into a pool of water, each pebble will generate a series of spreading ripples that sooner or later meet the oncoming ripples set in motion by other pebbles. The pool represents the Old World, with its basic *sapiens* population. Those points on the pool's surface where the pebbles land are points of transition to *Homo sapiens*, and the ripples are the migrations of *Homo sapiens*. This illustration has been used by several participants in the current debate; however, I now think it might not be correct. One reason for my caution is the existence of some important fossil specimens from a series of caves in Israel. Excavation at these sites has been going on sporadically for more than six decades, with Neanderthal fossils being found in some caves and modern human fossils in others. Until recently, the picture looked clear and supported the multiregional-evolution hypothesis. All the Neanderthal specimens – which came from the caves of Kebarra, Tabun, and Amud – were relatively old, perhaps some 60,000 years old. All the modern humans – which came from Skhul and Qafzeh – were younger, pehaps 40,000 to 50,000 years old. Given these dates, an evolutionary transformation in this region from the Neanderthal populations to the populations of modern humans looked plausible. Indeed, this sequence of fossils was one of the strongest pillars of support for the multiregional-evolution hypothesis.

In the late 1980s, however, this neat sequence was overturned. Researchers from Britain and France employed new methods of dating, known as electron spin resonance and thermoluminescence, on some of these fossils; both techniques depend on the decay of certain radioisotopes common in many rocks – a process that acts as an atomic clock for minerals in the rocks. The researchers found that the modern human fossils from Skhul and Qafzeh were older than most of the Neanderthal fossils, by as much as 40,000 years. If these results are correct, Neanderthals cannot be ancestors of modern humans, as the multi-regional-evolution model demands. What, then, is the alternative?

Instead of being the product of an evolutionary trend throughout the Old World, modern humans are seen in the alternative model as having arisen in a single geographical location. Bands of modern *Homo sapiens* would have migrated from this location and expanded into the rest of the Old World, replacing existing premodern populations. This model has had several labels, such as the 'Noah's Ark' hypothesis and the 'Garden of Eden' hypothesis. Most recently it has been called the 'Out of Africa' hypothesis, because sub-Saharan Africa has been identified as the most likely place where the first modern humans evolved. Several anthropologists have contributed to this view, and Christopher Stringer, of the Natural History Museum, London, is its most vigorous proponent.

The two models could hardly be more different: the multiregional-evolution model describes an evolutionary trend throughout the Old World toward modern *Homo sapiens*, with little population migration and no population replacement, whereas the 'Out of Africa' model calls for the evolution of *Homo sapiens* in one location only, followed by extensive population migration across the Old World, resulting in the replacement of existing premodern populations. Moreover, in the first model, modern geographical populations (what are known as 'races') would have deep genetic roots, having been essentially separate for as much as 2 million years; in the second model, these populations would have shallow genetic roots, all having derived from the single, recently evolved population in Africa.

The two models are also very different in their predictions of what we should see in the fossil record. According to the multiregional-evolution model, anatomical characteristics that we see in modern geographical populations should be visible in fossils in the same region, going back almost 2 million years, when *Homo erectus* first expanded its range beyond Africa. In the 'Out of Africa' model, no such regional continuity over time is expected; indeed, modern populations should share African characteristics, if anything.

Milford Wolpoff, the strongest proponent of the multi-   19 regional-evolution hypothesis, told an audience at the 1990 gathering of the American Association for the Advancement of Science that 'the case for anatomical continuity is clearly demonstrated.' In northern Asia, for instance, certain features, such as the shape of the face, the configuration of the cheekbones, and the shovel shape of the incisor teeth, can be seen in fossils 75,000 years old; in the famous Peking Man fossils, which are a quarter of a million years old; and in modern Chinese populations. Stringer acknowledges this, but he notes that these features are not confined to northern Asia and therefore cannot be taken as evidence of regional continuity.

Wolpoff and his colleagues make a similar argument for Southeast Asia and Australia. But, as Stringer points out, the supposed sequence of continuity is built on fossils dated at only three time points: 1.8 million, 100,000, and 30,000 years ago. This paucity of reference points, says Stringer, weakens the case in the extreme.

These examples illustrate the problems anthropologists face. Not only are there differences of opinion over the significance of important anatomical features, but, Neanderthals aside, the fossil record is much slimmer than most anthropologists would like (and than most nonanthropologists believe). Until these impediments are overcome, a consensus on the larger question may remain out of reach.

We can assess fossil anatomy from a different perspective, however. Neanderthals appear to have been stocky individuals with short limbs. This stature is an appropriate physical adaptation to the cold climatic conditions that prevailed throughout much of their range. The anatomy of the first modern humans in the same part of the world, however, is very different. These people were tall, slightly built, and long-limbed. A lithe body stature is much more suited to a tropical or temperate climate, not the frozen steppes of Ice Age Europe. This puzzle would be explicable if the first modern Europeans were descendants of migrants from Africa rather than having evolved in Europe, and the 'Out of Africa' model therefore derives some support from this observation.

It receives further support from another direct observation of the fossil record. If the multiregional-evolution hypothesis is correct, then we would expect to find early examples of modern humans appearing more or less simultaneously throughout the Old World. That's not what we see. The earliest-known modern human fossils probably come from southern Africa. I say 'probably' because not only are these fossils fragmentary parts of jaws but there is a degree of uncertainty about their true age. For instance, the fossils from Border Cave and Klasies River Mouth Cave, both in South Africa, are thought to be a little more than 100,000 years old, and are adduced as support by proponents of the 'Out of Africa' hypothesis. However, the modern human fossils from the caves of Qafzeh and Skhul are also close to 100,000 years old. It is possible, therefore, that modern humans first arose in northern Africa or the

Middle East, and then migrated from there. Most anthropologists favour a sub-Saharan origin, however, based on the overall weight of the evidence.

No fossils of modern humans of this age have been found anywhere else in the rest of Asia or Europe. If this reflects evolutionary reality and is not simply the perennial problem of a lamentably incomplete fossil record, then the 'Out of Africa' hypothesis does look reasonable.

The majority of population geneticists support this hypothesis as being the most biologically plausible. These scientists study the genetic profile within species, and how it might change through time. If populations of a species remain in geographical contact with each other, genetic changes that arise through mutation may spread throughout the entire region, by means of interbreeding. The genetic profile of the species will alter as a result, but overall the species will remain genetically unified. There is a different outcome if populations of a species have become geographically isolated from each other, perhaps because of a change in the course of a river or the opening of a desert. In this case, a genetic change that arises in one population will not be transferred to other populations. The isolated populations may therefore steadily become genetically different from one another, perhaps eventually becoming different subspecies, or even different species altogether. Population geneticists use mathematical models to calculate the rate at which genetic change may occur in populations of various sizes, and can therefore offer suggestions about what might have occurred in ancient times. Most population geneticists, including Luigi Luca Cavalli-Sforza, at Stanford, and Shahin Rouhani, of University College, London, who have commented extensively on the debate, are skeptical of the feasibility of the multiregional-evolution model. They note that the multiregional model requires extensive gene flow across large populations, linking them genetically while allowing evolutionary change to turn them into modern humans. And if new dates for Java Man fossils, announced early in 1994, are correct, *Homo erectus* expanded its range beyond Africa almost 2 million years ago. Therefore, not only would gene flow have to be maintained over a large geographical area, according to the multiregional-evolution model, it would also have to be maintained over a very long period of time. This, conclude most population geneticists, is simply unrealistic. With premodern populations spread across Europe, Asia, and Africa, there is a greater likelihood of producing geographical variants (such as we indeed see among archaic *sapiens*) than a cohesive whole.

We'll leave fossils aside for a while, and turn to behavior, by which I mean its tangible products, tools and art objects. We have to remember that the vast preponderance of human behavior in technologically primitive human groups is archeologically invisible. For instance, an initiation ritual led by a shaman would involve the telling of myths, chanting, dancing, and body decoration – and none of these activities would enter the archeological record. Therefore we need to keep reminding ourselves, when we find stone tools and carved or painted objects, that they give us only the narrowest of windows onto the ancient world.

What we would like to identify in the archeological record is some kind of signal of the modern human mind at work. And we would like that signal to throw some light on the competing hypothesis. For example, if the signal appeared in all regions of the Old World more or less simultaneously, we could say that the multiregional-evolution model describes the most likely manner in which modern humans evolved. If, instead, the signal appeared first in an isolated location and then gradually spread to the rest of the world, this would give weight to the alternative model. We would hope, of course, that the archeological signal would coincide with the pattern from the fossil record.

We saw in chapter 2 that the appearance of the genus *Homo* coincides roughly with the beginning of the archeological record, some 2.5 million years ago. We saw, too, that the increased complexity of stone-tool assemblages 1.4 million years ago, moving from the Oldowan industry to the Acheulean, followed soon upon the evolution of *Homo erectus*. The link between biology and behavior is therefore very close: simple tools were made by the earliest *Homo*; a jump in complexity occurred with the evolution of *Homo erectus*. That link is seen again with the appearance of archaic *sapiens*, some time after half a million years ago.

After more than a million years of relative stasis, the simple handaxe industry of *Homo erectus* gave way to a more complex technology fashioned on large flakes. And where the Acheulean industry had perhaps a dozen identifiable implements, the new technologies comprised as many as sixty. The biological novelty we see in the anatomy of the archaic *sapiens*, including the Neanderthals, is clearly accompanied by a new level of technological competence. Once the new technology had become established, however, it changed little. Stasis, not innovation, characterized the new era.

When change did come, however, it was dazzling – so dazzling that we should be aware that we might be blind to the reality behind it. About 35,000 years ago in Europe, people began making tools of the finest form, fashioned from delicately struck stone blades. For the first time, bone and antler were used as raw material for toolmaking. Tool kits now comprised more than one hundred items, and included implements for fashioning rough clothing and for engraving and sculpting. For the first time, tools became works of art: antler spear throwers, for example, were adorned with lifelike animal carvings. Beads and pendants appear in the fossil record, announcing the new practice of body decoration. And – most evocative of all – paintings on the walls of deep caves speak of a mental world we readily recognize as our own. Unlike previous eras, when statis dominated, innovation is now the essence of culture, with change being measured in millennia rather than hundreds of millennia. Known as the Upper Paleolithic Revolution, this collective archeological signal is unmistakable evidence of the modern human mind at work.

Now, I said that the archeological signal of the Upper Paleolithic Revolution might be blinding us to reality. By this I mean that for historical reasons the known archeological record in Western Europe is far richer than in Africa. For every archeological site of this era in Africa, there are about two hundred such sites in Western Europe. The disparity reflects a difference in the intensity of scientific exploration in the two continents, not the reality of human prehistory. For a long time, the Upper Paleolithic Revolution was taken as an indication that the final emergence of modern humans occurred in Western Europe. After all, the archeological signal and the fossil record coincided there precisely: both indicate a dramatic event about 35,000 years ago: modern humans appeared in Western Europe 35,000 years ago and their modern behavior is immediately part of the archeological record. Or so it was assumed.

Recently, this view has changed. Western Europe is now recognized as something of a backwater, and we can discern a transformation sweeping across Europe, from east to west. Beginning about 50,000 years ago, in Eastern Europe, the existing Neanderthal populations disappeared and were replaced by modern humans, the final replacement taking place in the far west by about 33,000 years ago. The coincidental appearance of modern humans and modern human behavior in Western Europe reflects the influx of a new kind of population, modern *Homo sapiens*. The Upper Paleolithic Revolution in Europe was a demographic signal and not an evolutionary signal.

If modern humans were migrating into Western Europe beginning 50,000 years ago, where did they come from? On the basis of the fossil evidence, we would say Africa, in all probability – or perhaps the Middle East. Despite the paucity of the archeological record, it does support an African origin of modern human behavior. Technologies based on narrow blades begin to appear on that continent around 100,000 years ago. This, remember, would coincide with the first known appearance of modern human anatomy, and could be taken as a third example of the link between biology and behavior.

The link here may, however, be an illusion, the result of happenstance. I say this because in the Middle East, where both the fossil and archeological records are good, we see something that is clear and yet paradoxical. The application of new dating techniques shows that Neanderthals and modern humans essentially coexisted in the region for as long as 60,000 years. (In 1989, the Tabun Neanderthal was shown to be at least 100,000 years old, making it a contemporary of the modern humans from Qafzeh and Skhul.) Throughout that time, the only form of tool technology we see is that associated with Neanderthals. The name given to their technology is Mousterian, after the cave of Le Moustier, in France, where it was first discov- 27 ered. The fact that the anatomically modern human populations in the Middle East appear to have manufactured Mousterianlike technology rather than the innovation-rich tool assemblages so characteristic of the Upper Paleolithic means that they were modern in form only, and not in their behavior. The link between anatomy and behavior therefore seems to break. The archeological signal of the earliest modern human behavior is weak and sporadic, and may be the victim of the poorly known record. Although blade-based technology is seen first in Africa, it isn't possible to point confidently to the African continent and say, 'This is where modern human behavior began,' and then trace its expansion into Eurasia.

The third line of evidence bearing on the origin of modern humans, that of molecular genetics, is the least equivocal. It is also the most controversial. During the 1980s, a new model of modern human origins emerged. Known as the mitochondrial Eve hypothesis, it essentially supported the 'Out of Africa' model, cogently so. Most proponents of the 'Out of Africa' hypothesis are prepared to entertain the possibility that as modern humans expanded from Africa to the rest of the Old World they interbred to some degree with established premodern populations. This would allow for some threads of genetic continuity from ancient populations through to modern ones. The mitochondrial Eve model, however, refutes this. According to this model, as modern populations migrated out of Africa and grew in numbers, they *completely replaced* existing premodern populations. Interbreeding between the immigrant and existing populations, if it occurred at all, did so to an infinitesimal degree.

The mitochondrial Eve model flowed from the work of two laboratories – that of Douglas Wallace and his colleagues at Emory University, and of Allan Wilson and his colleagues at the University of California, Berkeley. They scrutinized the genetic material, or DNA, that occurs in tiny organelles within the cell called mitochondria. When an egg from a mother and sperm from a father fuse, the only mitochrondria that become part of the cells of the newly formed embryo are from the egg. Therefore, mitochondrial DNA is inherited solely through the maternal line.

For several technical reasons, mitochondrial DNA is particularly suited to peering back through the generations in order to glimpse the course of evolution. And since the DNA is inherited through the maternal line, it eventually leads to a single ancestral female. According to the analyses, modern humans can trace their genetic ancestry to a female who lived in Africa perhaps 150,000 years ago. (It should be borne in mind, however, that this one female was part of a population of as many as 10,000 individuals; she was not a lone Eve with her Adam.)

Not only did the analyses indicate an African origin for modern humans, but they also revealed no evidence of interbreeding with premodern populations. All the samples of mitochondrial DNA analyzed so far from living human populations are remarkably similar to one another, indicating a common, recent origin. If genetic mixing between modern and archaic *sapiens* had occurred, some people would have mitochondrial DNA very different from the average, indicating its ancient origin. So far, with more than 4000 people from around the world having been tested, no such ancient mitochondrial DNA has been found. All the mitochondrial DNA types from modern populations that have been examined appear to be of recent origin. The implication is that modern newcomers completely replaced ancient populations – the process having begun in Africa 150,000 years ago and then having spread through Eurasia over the next 100,000 years.

When Allan Wilson and his team first published their results, in a January 1987 issue of *Nature*, the conclusions were stated boldly, provoking consternation among anthropologists and wide interest among the public. Wilson and his colleagues wrote that their data indicated that 'the transformation of archaic to modern forms of *Homo sapiens* occurred first in Africa, about 100,000 to 140,000 years ago, and . . . all present-day humans are descendants of that population.' (Later analyses produced slightly earlier dates.) Douglas Wallace and his colleagues generally supported the Berkeley group's conclusions.

Milford Wolpoff stuck to his multiregional model of evolution and denounced the data and analyses as unsound, but Wilson and his colleagues continued to produce more data and eventually stated that the conclusions were statistically unassailable. Recently, however, some statistical problems in the analysis were discovered, and the conclusions were recognized as being less concrete than had been asserted. Nevertheless, many molecular biologists still believe that the mitochondrial DNA data sufficiently support the 'Out of Africa' hypothesis. And it should be noted that more conventional genetic evidence, based on DNA in the nucleus, is beginning to reveal the same kind of pattern shown by the mitochondrial DNA data.

Those who promote the notion of complete or even partial replacement of premodern by modern populations have an uncomfortable issue to face: How did that replacement occur? According to Milford Wolpoff, such a scenario requires that we accepted violent genocide. We are familiar with killing of this nature in the decimation of Native American and Australian aborigine populations in the nineteenth century. And it may have been true in ancient times, too, although as yet there is not a shred of evidence for this.

Given the absence of evidence, we are forced to look for possible alternatives to the proposed one of violence. If none exists, then that hypothesis becomes stronger, though unproved. Ezra Zubrow, an anthropologist at the State University of New York, Buffalo, has pursued such an alternative model. He has developed computer models of interacting populations, in which one has a slight competitive edge over the other. By running such simulations he is able to determine what kind of advantage might be required by the superior population in order to replace the second very rapidly. The answer is counterintuitive: a 2 percent advantage can lead to the elimination of the second population within a millennium.

We can readily understand how one population might destroy another through military superiority. But it is much less easy for us to understand how a slight advantage in, for instance, exploiting resources such as food can play itself out over a relatively short period of time, yielding cataclysmic consequences. If modern humans had a slight advantage over Neanderthals, how are we to explain the apparent coexistence of these two populations for as much as 60,000 years in the Middle East? One explanation is that although modern humans had evolved in anatomical terms, modern human behavior followed later. A second, favored by many, is that the coexistence is more apparent than real. It is possible that the different populations occupied the region by turns, following climatic shifts. In colder times, modern humans moved south and the Neanderthals occupied the Middle East; in warmer times the reverse occurred. Because the time resolution of cave deposits is poor, this kind of 'sharing' of a locality can look like coexistence.

It's worth noting, however, that where we do know that Neanderthals and modern humans coexisted – in Western Europe, 35,000 years ago – they did so for a millennium or two at most, in accord with Zubrow's model. Zubrow's work does not demonstrate unequivocally that demographic competition was the means by which modern humans replaced premodern populations when they encountered them. But it does demonstrate that violence is not the sole candidate as the mechanism for replacement.

Where does all this leave us? The important issue of the origin of modern humans remains unresolved, despite the welter of information that has been brought to bear. My sense of it, however, is that the multiregional-evolution hypothesis is unlikely to be correct. I suspect that modern *Homo sapiens* arose as a discrete evolutionary event, somewhere in Africa; but I suspect, too, that when descendants of these first modern humans expanded into Eurasia, they intermixed with the populations there. Why the genetic evidence, as currently interpreted, doesn't reflect this, I don't know. Perhaps the current reading of the evidence is incorrect. Or perhaps the mitochondrial Eve hypothesis will turn out to be right, after all. This uncertainty is more likely to be resolved when the clamor of debate ebbs and new evidence is found in support of one or another of the competing hypotheses.

The Language of Art

There is no question that some of the most potent relics of human prehistory are the depictions of animals and humans – carved, painted, or sculpted – produced within the past 30,000 years. By this time, modern humans had evolved and had occupied much of the Old World, but probably not yet the New World. Wherever people lived – in Africa, in Asia, in Europe, and in Australia – they produced images of their world. The urge to produce depictions was apparently irresistible, and the images themselves are irresistibly evocative. They are also mysterious.

One of my most memorable experiences as an anthropologist was visiting some of the decorated caves in southwest France in 1980. I was making a series of films for BBC television and so had the opportunity to see what few have been able to see, including the famous cave of Lascaux, near the town of Les Eyzies, in the Dordogne. The most extensively decorated of all caves from Ice Age Europe, Lascaux has been closed to the public since 1963, to protect the integrity of the paintings; currently there is a tight restriction of five visitors a day. Fortunately, a brilliantly rendered duplicate of the cave's decorated walls has recently been completed, so that the images may still be viewed. My visit to the real Lascaux in 1980 recalled for me a time, three and a half decades ago, when I visited the cave with my parents and Henri Breuil, France's most famous prehistorian. The images of bulls, horses, and deer were as transfixing on this occasion as they were when I was a youth, as they seem to move before one's eyes.

As spectacular as Lascaux is, the cave of the Tuc d'Audoubert, in the Ariège region of France, is unique and arresting. The cave is one of three decorated caves on land owned by Count Robert Bégouën. A narrow, winding passageway leads from bright sunlight several kilometers into the deepest gloom. The count's flashlight brings the walls to light with dancing shadows, and the clay floor glows orange. Eventually one reaches a small rotunda at the end of the passageway, and the count shines his light with appropriate drama on a spot at the center of the chamber, the ceiling sloping low to the floor beyond. There, one sees the figures of two bison, superbly sculpted from clay, resting against rocks.

I had seen pictures of these famous figures, of course, but nothing prepared me for reality. Measuring about one-sixth normal size, they were perfect in form, full of movement in their motionlessness; they encapsulate life. The skill of the artists who sculpted these figures 15,000 years ago is breathtaking, especially when one remembers the conditions under which they must have worked. Using simple lamps charged with animal fat, they carried clay from a neighboring chamber and created the animals' form with their fingers and some kind of flat implement; eyes, nostrils, mouth, and mane were created with a sharp stick or bone. After they had finished, they carefully cleared away most of the debris of their work, leaving only a few sausage-shaped pieces of clay. Once interpreted as phalluses or horns, these are now thought to have been samplers, on which the sculptors tested the plasticity of the clay.

The reasons for creating the bison and the circumstances under which bison were crafted are lost in time. A third figure is crudely engraved in the floor of the cave near the other two, and there is another statuette, small and again in clay. Most intriguing, however, are heel prints, probably those of children, around the figures. Were the children playing while the artists worked? If so, why do we not see footprints of the artists? Were the heel prints made during a ritual, encapsulating some part of Upper Paleolithic mythology in which the bison figures were the central part? We do not know, perhaps even cannot know. As the South African archeologist David Lewis-Williams says of prehistoric art, 'Meaning is always culturally bound.'

Lewis-Williams, who works at the University of the Witwatersrand, has been studying the art of the !Kung San people of the Kalahari, with an eye toward illuminating the meaning of prehistoric art, including that of Ice Age Europe. He recognizes that artistic expression may form an enigmatic thread in the intricate weave of the cultural fabric of a society. Mythology, music, and dance are also part of that fabric: each thread contributes meaning to the whole, but by themselves they are necessarily incomplete.

Even if we were to witness the slice of Upper Paleolithic life in which the cave paintings played their role, would we understand the meaning of the whole? I doubt it. We have only to think of the stories related in modern religions to appreciate the importance of cryptic symbols that may be meaningless outside the culture to which they belong. Think of the meaningfulness to a Christian of an image of a man holding a staff, with a lamb at his feet. And think of the absence of any such meaning to someone who has not heard the Christian story.

Mine is not a message of despair but of caution. The ancient images we have today are fragments of an ancient story, and although the urge to know what they mean is great, it is wise to accept the probable limits of our understanding. Moreover, there has been a strong, and probably inevitable, Western bias in the perception of prehistoric art. One consequence has been a lack of attention to prehistoric art of equal and sometimes greater antiquity in eastern and southern Africa. Another has been to view the art in the Western way: as though it consisted of pictures hung on a museum wall, as objects simply to view. Indeed, the great French prehistorian André Leroi-Gourhan once described the images of the Ice Age as 'the origins of Western art.' This is clearly not the case, because at the end of the Ice Age, 10,000 years ago, representational paintings and engravings all but disappeared, to be replaced by schematic images and geometric patterns. Many of the techniques that had been applied in Lascaux, such as perspective and a sense of movement, had to be reinvented in Western art with the Renaissance.

Before we examine some of the attempts to gain a glimpse of Upper Paleolithic life through the medium of ancient images, we should sketch an overall view of Ice Age art. The period in question began 35,000 years ago, and ended some 10,000 years ago, with the end of the Ice Age itself. This period, remember, witnessed the first appearance in Western Europe of sophisticated technology, which evolved rapidly, as if following fashion. The sequence of changes is marked by names given to each new variation of Upper Paleolithic technology, and we can look at the changes in Ice Age art using the same framework.

The Upper Paleolithic essentially begins with the Aurignacian period, from 34,000 to 30,000 years ago. Although there are no known painted caves from this period, the people devoted considerable effort to making small ivory beads, presumably for decorating clothes. They also produced exquisite human and animal figures, usually carved from ivory. For instance, half a dozen tiny ivory figures of mammoths and horses have been recovered from the site of Vogelherd, in Germany. One of the horse figures is as skillfully produced a piece as can be found throughout the

Upper Paleolithic. As I've said, music surely played an important part in these people's lives, and a small bone flute from the Abri Blanchard, in southwestern France, is testimony to that.

The people of the Gravettian period, from 30,000 to 22,000 years ago, were the first to manufacture clay figurines, some of which were animal and some human. Cave paintings in this period of the Upper Paleolithic are rare, but negative handprints are found in some caves, perhaps made by holding the hand up to the cave wall and blowing paint around the edges. (A slightly macabre example of this practice has been found at the site of Gargas, in the French Pyrenees, where more than two hundred prints have been counted, almost all of them missing one or more parts of fingers.) The most famous of the Gravettian innovations, however, are the female figures, often lacking facial features and lower legs. Made from clay, ivory, or calcite, and found throughout much of Europe, they have typically been called Venuses, and have been assumed to represent a continent-wide female fertility cult. Recent and more critical scrutiny, however, shows a great deal of diversity in the form of these figures, and few scholars would now argue for the fertility-cult idea.

Cave painting, which generally captures most attention, began in the Solutrean period of the Upper Paleolithic, from 22,000 to 18,000 years ago. Other forms of artistic expression are more prominent, however. For instance, the carving of large, impressive bas-reliefs, often at living sites, 39 was evidently important to the Solutreans. A wonderful example is at the site of Roc de Sers, in the Charente region of France, where large figures of horses, bison, reindeer, mountain goats, and one human were cut into the rock at the back of a shelter; some of the figures stand out six inches or so in relief.

The final period of the Upper Paleolithic – the Magdalenian, from 18,000 to 11,000 years ago – was the era of deep-cave painting: 80 percent of all painted caves date from this period. Lascaux was painted during this time, as was Altamira, a similarly spectacular cave in the Cantabrian region of northern Spain. The Magdalenians were also talented sculptors and engravers of stone, bone, and ivory objects – some utilitarian, such as spear throwers, some not obviously so, such as 'batons.' Although it is often said that the human form is a rarity in Ice Age art, in the Magdalenian period this was not the case. Magdalenian people at the cave of La Marche, in southwestern France, engraved more than a hundred profiles of human heads, each so individualistic as to give the impression of a portrait.

The spectacular painted ceiling of Altamira might have forever remained undiscovered but for Maria, the young daughter of Don Marcellion de Sautuola, who owned the farm where the cave is located. One day in 1879, father and daughter explored the cave, which had been discovered a decade earlier. Maria entered a low chamber that de

Sautuola had explored previously. She was 'running about in the cavern and playing about here and there,' she later recalled. 'Suddenly [she] made out forms and figures on the roof. . . . "Look, Papa, oxen," ' she cried. In the flickering light of an oil lamp, she saw what no one had seen for 17,000 years; images of two dozen bison grouped in a circle, with two horses, a wolf, three boars, and three female deer around the periphery. They were in red, yellow, and black, appearing as fresh as if they had just been painted.

An enthusiastic amateur archeologist, Maria's father was astonished to see what he had missed and his daughter had found, and recognized it as a great discovery. Unfortunately, the professional prehistorians of the day did not: the paintings were so bright and vital that they were considered to be the work of a recent artist. They looked too good, too realistic, too artistic to be the work of primitive minds. Instead, they must have been done by a recent itinerant artist.

At this time, several pieces of portable art – that is, engraved and carved bone and antler – had been discovered. Prehistoric art had therefore been recognized as real. But no paintings had been accepted as ancient. Ironically, just before the images of Altamira were discovered, Léopold Chiron, a schoolteacher, found engravings on the walls in the cave of Chabot, in southwestern France. The engravings were difficult to decipher, however. Prehistorians were reluctant to accept them as evidence of Upper

Paleolithic wall art. As the British archeologist Paul Bahn has observed, 'Whereas the pictures of Chabot were too modest to make an impact, those of Altamira were too splendid to be believed.'

When de Sautuola died in 1888, Altamira was still dismissed as a transparent attempt at fraud. The final acceptance of Altamira as genuinely prehistoric was brought about by a steady accumulation of similar finds, albeit of lesser impact – principally in France. Most important among these was the Cave of La Mouthe, in the Dordogne region of France. Excavations beginning in 1895 and continuing to the turn of the century revealed wall art, such as an engraved bison and several painted images. Deposits of Upper Paleolithic age covered some of these images, proving them to be ancient. Furthermore, the first example of a Paleolithic lamp, carved from sandstone, was discovered in the cave, providing a means by which cave artists could work. Professional opinion began to turn, and very soon Upper Paleolithic painting was accepted as a reality. The most famous landmark of that acceptance was a paper by Émile Carthailac, a leading opponent of the paintings' authenticity, called 'Mea Culpa d'un Sceptique,' published in 1902. 'We no longer have any reason to doubt Altamira,' he wrote. Although Carthailac's paper has become a classic example of a scientist's admitting his mistake, its tone is actually rather grudging, and he defends his earlier skepticism.

At first, the Ice Age paintings were viewed as 'simple idle

doodlings, graffiti, play activity: mindless decoration by hunters with time on their hands,' as Bahn puts it. This interpretation, he says, stems from the conception of art in contemporary France: 'Art was still seen in terms of recent centuries, with their portraits, landscapes and narrative pictures. It was simply "art," its sole function was to please and to decorate.' Moreover, some influential French prehistorians were sharply anticlerical and did not like to impute religious expression to Upper Paleolithic people. This early interpretation can be seen as reasonable, especially as the first examples of art – portable objects – indeed looked simple. With the later discovery of wall art, however, this view changed. The paintings did not reflect real life, in the relative numbers of animals on the roof and on the wall; and there were enigmatic images, too, geometric signs without obvious representation.

John Halverson, of the University of California, Santa Cruz, has recently proposed that prehistorians should return to the 'art for art's sake' interpretation. We should not expect human consciousness to emerge full-blown during our evolution, he reasons, so that the first examples of art in prehistory are likely to be simplistic because the people's minds were cognitively simple. The Altamira paintings do look simplistic: depictions of horses, bison, and other animals appear as single individuals or sometimes as groups, but only rarely in anything that approaches a naturalistic setting. The images are accurate but devoid of context. This, says Halverson, indicates that the Ice Age artists were simply painting or engraving fragments of their environment, in the complete absence of any mythological meaning.

I find this argument unconvincing. Just a few examples of the images of the Ice Age are sufficient to indicate that there's more to the art than the first halting workings of the modern mind. For instance, in one of the other caves owned by Count Bégouën, the cave of Trois Frères, is an image of a human/animal chimera, known as the Sorcerer. The creature stands on its hind legs, its face turned to stare out of the wall. Sporting a large pair of antlers, it seems to be made of the body parts of many different animals, including human. This is not a simple image, 'unmediated by cognitive reflection,' as Halverson would have us believe. And neither is the first creature in the Hall of Bulls in Lascaux. Known as the Unicorn, the creature may be meant as a human disguised as an animal or may be a chimera. Many such drawings are sufficient to convince us that we are seeing images greatly mediated by cognitive reflection.

Most significant, however, is that the images are more complex than Halverson implies. As I've indicated, the paintings and engravings are not of naturalistic scenes from the Ice Age world. There is nothing like a true landscape painting. And, to judge from the remains of animals at the living sites of these people, neither are the depictions a simple reflection of daily diet. The Upper Paleolithic painters had horses and bison on their minds, whereas they had reindeer and ptarmigan in their stomachs. The fact that some animals are far more prominent as images on cave walls than they were in the landscape is surely significant: they appear to have had a special importance to the Paleolithic people who painted them.

The first major hypothesis to explain why Upper Paleolithic people painted what they did adduced hunting magic. At the turn of the century, anthropologists were learning that Australian aboriginal paintings were part of magical and totemic rituals designed to improve the spoils of a forthcoming hunt. In 1903, the historian of religions Salomon Reinach argued that the same could be true of Upper Paleolithic art: in both societies, paintings overrepresented a few species in relation to the natural environment. Upper Paleolithic people may have made paintings to ensure the increase of totemic and prey animals, just as the Australians were known to do.

Henri Breuil liked Reinach's ideas, and developed and promoted them vigorously during his long career. For almost sixty years, he recorded, mapped, copied, and counted images in the caves throughout Europe. He also developed a chronology for the evolution of art during the Upper Paleolithic. During this time, Breuil continued to interpret the art as hunting magic, as did the majority of the archeological establishment.

An obvious problem with the hunting-magic hypothesis was that the images depicted very often did not, as noted, reflect the diet of the Upper Paleolithic painters. The French anthropologist Claude Lévi-Strauss once noted that in the art of the Kalahari San and the Australian aborigines certain animals were depicted most frequently not because they were 'good to eat' but because they were 'good to think.' When Breuil died in 1961, it was time for the emergence of a new perspective, which came from André Leroi-Gourhan, who was to become as prominent in French prehistory as Breuil had been.

Leroi-Gourhan looked for structure in the art, seeking meaning in patterns of many images, not in individual images as Breuil had done. He conducted lengthy surveys of the painted caves and came to see repeated patterns, with certain animals 'occupying' certain parts of the caves. Deer, for instance, often appeared in entranceways but were uncommon in main chambers. Horse, bison, and ox were the predominant creatures of the main chambers. Carnivores mostly occurred deep in the cave system. Moreover, some animals represented maleness, some femaleness, he said. The horse image represented maleness, and the bison femaleness; the stag and the ibex were also male; the mammoth and the ox were female. To Leroi-Gourhan, the order in the paintings reflected an ordering in Upper Paleolithic society: namely, the division between maleness and femaleness. Another French archeologist, Annette Laming-Emperaire, developed a similar concept of male-female duality. However, the two scholars often disagreed over which images represented maleness and which femaleness. This difference of opinion contributed to the eventual downfall of the scheme.

The notion that the caves themselves might impose structure on artistic expression has recently been revived, but in a most unusual way. The French archeologists Iégor Reznikoff and Michel Dauvois conducted detailed surveys of three decorated caves in the Ariège region of southwest France. Unconventionally, they were not looking for stone tools, engraved objects, or new paintings. They were singing. More specifically, they moved slowly through the caves, stopping repeatedly to test the resonance of each section. Using notes spanning three octaves, they drew up a resonance map of each cave and discovered that those areas with highest resonance were also those most likely to harbor a painting or engraving. In their report, which they published at the end of 1988, Reznikoff and Dauvois commented on the stunning impact of cave resonance, an experience that would have surely been enhanced in the flickering light of simple lamps back in the Ice Age.

It requires little imagination to think of Upper Paleolithic people chanting incantations in front of cave paintings. The unusual nature of the images, and the fact that they are often deep in the most inaccessible parts of caves, begs the suggestion of ritual. When one stands in front of an Ice Age creation now, as I did with the bison of Le Tuc d'Audoubert, the ancient voices force themselves on one's mind, with an accompaniment, perhaps, of drums, flutes, and whistles. Reznikoff and Dauvois's is a fascinating discovery that, as the Cambridge University archeologist Chris

47

Scarre commented at the time, draws 'new attention to the likely importance of music and singing in the rituals of our early ancestors.'

When Leroi-Gourhan died in 1986, prehistorians were again ready for a major rethinking of their interpretations, just as had happened when Breuil died. These days, researchers are prepared to entertain a diversity of explanations, but in all cases the cultural context is emphasized and there is a greater awareness of the danger of imposing ideas from modern society on Upper Paleolithic society.

Almost certainly, at least some elements of Ice Age art concerned the way Upper Paleolithic people organized their ideas about their world – an expression of their spiritual cosmos. We'll come to this again a little later. But there may have been more practical aspects in the way they organized their social and economic worlds. Margaret Conkey, an anthropologist at the University of California, Berkeley, has suggested, for instance, that Altamira might have been a fall gathering place for many hundreds of people from the region. Red deer and limpets would have been abundant then, and this would have provided ample economic justification for such an aggregation of bands. But, as we know from modern hunter-gatherers, such aggregations, whatever the ostensible economic reason, are more for social and political alliance building than for mundane practicalities.

The British anthropologist Robert Laden believes that he can perceive something of the structure of such alliances in the cave sites in northern Spain. The major sites, such as Altamira, are often surrounded by smaller sites within a 10-mile radius, as if they were centers of political or social alliance. The 20-mile diameter of such a sphere may represent the optimum distance over which alliances could readily be maintained. No such patterning has yet been discerned among the cave sites of France.

Perhaps the arrangement of bison and other animal images on the painted ceiling of Altamira depicts the center's sphere of influence in some way. The main structure of the painted ceiling consists of almost two dozen polychrome images of bison, arranged principally around the periphery. These, suggests Margaret Conkey, may represent the different groups that aggregate at the site. Significantly, the range of engraved objects that archeologists have found at Altamira seems to be a sampling of many local decorative forms. Throughout northern Spain at this time, people decorated utilitarian objects with various designs, including chevrons, lunate structures, nested curves, and so on. About fifteen such designs have been identified, each of which tends to be geographically restricted, suggesting local styles or band identities. At Altamira, many of these local styles are found together, hence the argument for an aggregation site of some social and political importance. So far, no such evidence has been uncovered at Lascaux. It is reasonable, however, to think of the site as having considerable importance to people over a wide area, rather than as the local product of enthusiastic 49 painters. Perhaps Lascaux derived its power as the location of an important spiritual event, such as the appearance of a deity in the Upper Paleolithic cosmos. Such is the case with many otherwise sterile parts of the environment for the Australian aborigines, for example.

I've already said that the images in Ice Age art are of animals plucked from their ecological context, and in proportions that do not represent their occurrence in the real world. This in itself tells us something of the enigmatic nature of the art. In addition to the repesentational images, however, there are other markings that are even more enigmatic: a scattering of geometric patterns – or signs, as they have been called. They include dots, grids, chevrons, curves, zigzags, nested curves, and rectangles, and are among the most puzzling elements of Upper Paleolithic art. For the most part, they have been explained as components of whatever hypothesis prevailed, in hunting magic, for instance, or the maleness/femaleness dichotomy. David Lewis-Williams has recently offered a new and interesting interpretation: they are the telltale signs of shamanistic art, he says – images from a mind in the state of hallucination.

Lewis-Williams has studied the art of the San people of southern Africa for four decades. Much of their art dates back to perhaps 10,000 years ago, but some was created within recent historical memory. Gradually, he came to realize that the images of San art were not simpleminded presentations of San life, as Western anthropologists had long assumed. Instead, they were the product of shamans in a state of trance: the images were a connection with a shamanistic spirit world and were depictions of what the shaman saw during his hallucination. At one point in his studies, Lewis-Williams and his colleague Thomas Dowson interviewed an old woman who lived in the Tsolo district of the Transkei. The daughter of a shaman, she described some of the now-vanished shamanistic rituals.

Shamans may induce trance in themselves by various techniques, including drugs and hyperventilation, she said. However it was achieved, the trance state was almost always accompanied by the rhythmic singing, dancing and clapping of groups of women. As the trance deepens, the shamans begin to tremble, their arms and bodies virogously vibrating. While visiting the spirit world, the shaman often 'dies,' bending over as if in pain. The eland is a potent force in San mythology, and the shaman may use blood from cuts in the neck and throat of the animal to infuse potency into someone by rubbing it into cuts on the person's neck and throat. Later, the shaman often uses some of the same blood while painting a record of his hallucinatory contact with the spirit world. The images have a potency of their own, derived from the context in which they were painted, and the old woman told Lewis-Williams that some of the power could be acquired by placing one's hand on them.

The eland is the most frequently depicted animal in San paintings, and its potency comes in many forms. Lewis-Williams wondered whether the horse and the bison were similar sources of potency for the Upper Paleolithic people – images that were appealed to and touched when spiritual energy was rquired. As a way of approaching this question, he needed evidence that Upper Paleolithic art, too, was shamanistic. A clue lay with the geometric signs.

According to the psychological literature that Lewis-Williams surveyed, there are three stages of hallucination, each one deeper and more complex. In the first stage, the subject sees geometric forms, such as grids, zigzags, dots, spirals, and curves. These images, six forms in all, are shimmering, incandescent, mercurial – and powerful. They are called entoptic ('within vision') images, because they are produced by the basic neural architecture of the brain. 'Because they derive from the human nervous system, all people who enter certain altered states of consciousness, no matter what their cultural background, are liable to perceive them,' Lewis-Williams pointed out in a 1986 article in *Current Anthropology*. In the second stage of trance, people begin to see these images as real objects. Curves may be construed as hills in a landscape, chevrons as weapons, and so on. The nature of what the individual sees depends on the individual's cultural experience and concerns. San shamans frequently manipulate series of curves into images of honeycombs, since bees are a symbol of supernatural power that these people harness when entering a trance.

The passage from the second to the third stage of the hallucination is often accompanied by a sensation of traversing a vortex or rotating tunnel, and full-blown images – some commonplace, some extraordinary – may be seen. One type of important image during this stage is of human/animal chimera, or therianthropes, as they are called. These creatures are common in shamanistic San art. They are also an intriguing component of Upper Paleolithic art.

The entoptic images of stage-one hallucination are present in San art, which may be taken as objective evidence that the art is shamanistic. And these same images are to be seen in Upper Paleolithic art, sometimes superimposed on animals, sometimes in isolation. In combination with the presence of enigmatic therianthropes, they are strong evidence that at least some of Upper Paleolithic art is indeed shamanistic. These therianthropes were once dismissed as the product of 'a primitive mentality [that] failed to establish definitive boundaries between humans and animals,' as John Halverson put it. If, instead, they are images experienced in a trance, they were as real to the Upper Paleolithic painter as horses and bison.

When we think of art, we tend to think of a painting being made on a surface, whether it is a canvas or a wall. Shamanistic art is not like that. Shamans often perceive their hallucinations as emerging from rock surfaces: 'They see the images as having been put there by the spirits, and in painting them, the shamans say they are simply touching and marking what already exists,' Lewis-Williams explains. 'The first depictions were therefore not representational images in the way you or I think of them, but were fixed mental images of another world.' The rock surface itself, he notes, is an interface between the real world and the spirit world – a passageway between the two. It is more than a medium for the images; it is an essential part of the images and the ritual that went on there. Lewis-Williams' hypothesis has attracted a good deal of attention and, inevitably, some skepticism. Its value is in allowing us to see the art through different eyes. Shamanistic art is so very different from Western art in its execution and its construal that through it we can look at Upper Paleolithic art in new ways.

The French archeologist Michel Lorblanchet is also making us look at Upper Paleolithic art in different ways. For several years he has been doing experimental archeology, replicating images from the caves in an attempt to get a sense of the Ice Age artists' tasks and experience. His most ambitious project was to re-create the horses of Pêche Merle, a cave in the Lot region of France. The two horses face away from each other, rumps slightly overlapping, and stand about four feet tall. They have black and red dots on them and stencils of hands around them. Because the rock surface on which the images were painted is rough, the artists apparently delivered the paint by blowing it through a tube rather than using a brush.

Lorblanchet found a similar rock surface in a nearby cave and determined to paint the horses anew, using a blowing technique. 'I spent seven hours a day for a week, puff . . .

puff . . . puff,' he told a writer for *Discover*. 'It was exhausting, particularly because there was carbon monoxide in the cave. But you experience something special, painting like that. You feel you are breathing the image onto the rock – projecting your spirit from the deepest part of your body onto the rock surface.' This doesn't sound like a very scientific approach, but perhaps so elusive an intellectual target requires unorthodox methods. Lorblanchet has been innovative in the past, with his previous ventures into replication. This one surely deserves consideration, too. If the paintings of the Ice Age were part of Upper Paleolithic mythology, then the painters did put their spirit onto the wall, no matter what method they used to apply the paint.

We may never know what the Tuc d'Audoubert sculptors had in mind when they fashioned the bison, nor the painters at Lascaux when they drew the Unicorn, nor any of the Ice Age artists in what they did. But we can be sure that what they did was important in a very deep sense to the artists and to the people who saw the images in the generations afterward. The language of art is powerful to those who understand it, and puzzling to those who do not. What we do know is that here was the modern human mind at work, spinning symbolism and abstraction in a way that only *Homo sapiens* is capable of doing. Although we cannot yet be sure of the process by which modern humans evolved, we do know that it involved the emergence of the kind of mental world each of us experiences today.

Phoenix 60p Paperbacks

History/Biograpy/Travel

The Empire of Rome A.D. 98–190 *Edward Gibbon*
The Prince *Machiavelli*
The Alan Clark Diaries: Thatcher's Fall *Alan Clark*
Churchill: Embattled Hero *Andrew Roberts*
The French Revolution *E.J. Hobsbawm*
Voyage Around the Horn *Joshua Slocum*
The Great Fire of London *Samuel Pepys*
Utopia *Thomas More*
The Holocaust *Paul Johnson*
Tolstoy and History *Isaiah Berlin*

Science and Philosophy

A Guide to Happiness *Epicurus*
Natural Selection *Charles Darwin*
Science, Mind & Cosmos *John Brockman, ed.*
Zarathustra *Friedrich Nietzsche*
God's Utility Function *Richard Dawkins*
Human Origins *Richard Leakey*
Sophie's World: The Greek Philosophers *Jostein Gaarder*
The Rights of Woman *Mary Wollstonecraft*
The Communist Manifesto *Karl Marx & Friedrich Engels*
Birds of Heaven *Ben Okri*

Fiction

Riot at Misri Mandi *Vikram Seth*
The Time Machine *H. G. Wells*
Love in the Night *F. Scott Fitzgerald*

The Murders in the Rue Morgue *Edgar Allan Poe*
The Necklace *Guy de Maupassant*
You Touched Me *D. H. Lawrence*
The Mabinogion *Anon*
Mowgli's Brothers *Rudyard Kipling*
Shancarrig *Maeve Binchy*
A Voyage to Lilliput *Jonathan Swift*

POETRY
Songs of Innocence and Experience *William Blake*
The Eve of Saint Agnes *John Keats*
High Waving Heather *The Brontes*
Sailing to Byzantium *W. B. Yeats*
I Sing the Body Electric *Walt Whitman*
The Ancient Mariner *Samuel Taylor Coleridge*
Intimations of Immortality *William Wordsworth*
Palgrave's Golden Treasury of Love Poems *Francis Palgrave*
Goblin Market *Christina Rossetti*
Fern Hill *Dylan Thomas*

LITERATURE OF PASSION
Don Juan *Lord Byron*
From Bed to Bed *Catullus*
Satyricon *Petronius*
Love Poems *John Donne*
Portrait of a Marriage *Nigel Nicolson*
The Ballad of Reading Gaol *Oscar Wilde*
Love Sonnets *William Shakespeare*
Fanny Hill *John Cleland*
The Sexual Labyrinth (for women) *Alina Reyes*
Close Encounters (for men) *Alina Reyes*